larva

Adult female laying eggs

The larvae feed on the pulp of apples and pears.

Codling Moth, Carpocapsa pomonella

Chinese Silkworm, Bombyx mori. Raised for silk in Asia since 2600 B.C.; in Europe since A.D. 560. Silk is obtained by unwinding the cocoons.

egg

larva

adult

cocoon

BUTTERFLIES AND MOTHS

BY DR. WALTER ROBERT CORTI

ILLUSTRATED BY WALTER LINSENMAIER

THE ODYSSEY PRESS · NEW YORK

The male and female of Teinopalpus imperialis, *Asia*, are very different in shape and color. Such sexual dimorphism has frequently misled scientists into describing the two sexes as two different species.

Not all forms of life have the power to fascinate us; not everything in nature is equally pleasing to the eye. In the plant and animal kingdoms we find some forms which may repel us and some which may even frighten us. We also find some which, even before we have learned much about them, give us joy because of their beauty. And, beyond any question, of all living things, butterflies and moths are among the loveliest. The enchanting colors of their wings, their intimate commerce with the quiet flowers, their modest food needs, the innocence of their courtships make them seem like fairy creatures from some unspoiled paradise. They are a delight to curious children, harmless idlers, contented topers, and strolling lovers wherever they appear. It is as if they were created solely to make the world more beautiful. ■ About 100,000 species are known, including tiny varieties with a wingspread of less than a tenth of an inch, and giants whose wingspread may be as much as 12 inches. ■ They are found nearly everywhere in the world, but reach their highest forms of development in the tropics. ■ Butterflies and moths occur in the folklore of many peoples. According to a Greek myth, Psyche, the personification of the soul, had the wings of a butterfly, and the Greeks thought that butterflies were departed souls. Even today the lovely butterfly symbol is found on gravestones in some countries. ■ Yet these winged creatures could signify evil,

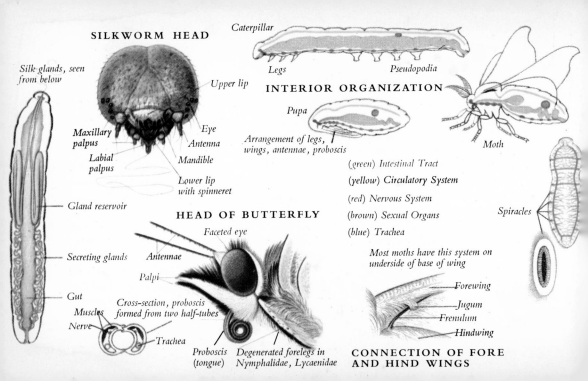

SILKWORM HEAD

Caterpillar

Legs   *Pseudopodia*

Silk-glands, seen from below

Upper lip

Maxillary palpus   *Eye*

Antenna

Labial palpus   *Mandible*

Lower lip with spinneret

Gland reservoir

Secreting glands

Gut

INTERIOR ORGANIZATION

Pupa

Arrangement of legs, wings, antennae, proboscis

Moth

(green) *Intestinal Tract*

(yellow) *Circulatory System*

(red) *Nervous System*

(brown) *Sexual Organs*

(blue) *Trachea*

Spiracles

Most moths have this system on underside of base of wing

HEAD OF BUTTERFLY

Faceted eye

Antennae

Palpi

Cross-section, proboscis formed from two half-tubes

Muscles

Nerve

Trachea

Proboscis (tongue)

Degenerated forelegs in Nymphalidae, Lycaenidae

Forewing

Jugum

Frenulum

Hindwing

CONNECTION OF FORE AND HIND WINGS

too. Folk tradition says that if a "plague moth" alights on a person, he will catch the plague. ■ In Rumania, it was said that butterflies come from the tears of the Virgin Mary. ■ The origin of the word butterfly is not known, but it is thought that it may come from the butter-yellow color of many of the familiar species. ■ Butterflies and moths belong to the class *Insecta*, the largest group of animals in the world. All insects have head, thorax, and abdomen separated by definite incisions; hence their name, from the Latin *insectum* meaning "cut in." Another characteristic of insects is that they have 6 articulated legs made up of several jointed segments. ■ Within this class, butterflies and moths are put in the order Lepidoptera, the scale-wings, from the Greek *lepis*, meaning "scale," and *pteron*, meaning "wing." ■ Most Lepidoptera, in the adult stage, have two pairs of scale-covered wings. In many, the fore wings are larger than the hind wings. ■ In general, butterflies are creatures of the day; moths those of the night. However, there are butterflies that fly at dusk, and moths that fly in the day. Most butterflies have long, slender antennae which are clubbed at the tip. The antennae of moths are rarely clubbed, but they may be feathery or threadlike. Butterflies usually rest with their wings folded over their back; moths rest with wings outstretched or folded by their sides. ■ Scientists believe they have discovered most of the birds and mammals in the world, but that there may be thousands of insects as yet undiscovered and therefore unclassified. Certainly there are new species of butterflies and moths still being found in many areas. Also, of the Lepidoptera known and classified by scientists, there are many, especially those found in remote areas, whose life histories remain to be studied. ■

9

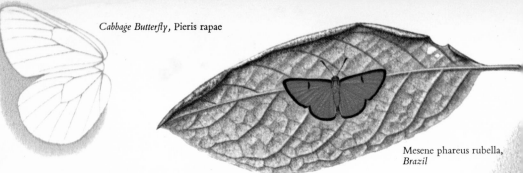

Cabbage Butterfly, Pieris rapae

Mesene phareus rubella, *Brazil*

Primitive genera generally have more complex wing venation than more highly developed genera.

Ghost Moth, Hepialus humili

■ Entomologists by no means agree on the classification of all butterflies and moths. Classification of a single species of Lepidoptera is based on differences in the venation of the wings, on characteristic peculiarities of the legs, of the antennae, of the sexual apparatus, of the mouth parts, and even of the hearing organs. Using these criteria, entomologists have grouped the various species into about 100 families. In some

Ancyluris aulestes pandama, *Peru*

Mesosemia croesus, *Brazil*

Helicopis acis, *Brazil*

Wing venation shows that these five species all belong to the same family.

Zeonia faunus, *Peru*

families—such as the whites, which include a large group of butterflies—most of the species look very much alike. In other families, the species may look amazingly different. But even within the species there may be differences. Male and female do not always look alike. In the Orgyia, Solenobia, and Psychidae groups, for instance, only the male can fly. The females either have no wings or have stub wings which are useless. ∎

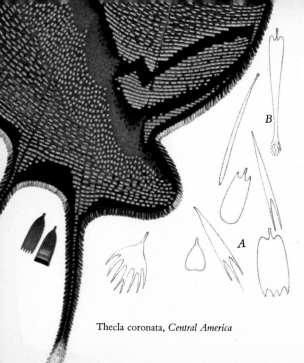

Thecla coronata, *Central America*

A distinguishing feature of adult butterflies and moths is their four scale-covered wings. The scales overlap like shingles on a roof. The shapes of the scales vary, and several kinds may be found on the same wing. ■ In some species, the mottled splendor of the wing colors results from actual pigments in the scales. In others, the blues, violets and greens, as well as the over-all iridescence, are created solely by the refraction of light on the scales. To achieve such nuances of color, an astonishing variety of physical and chemical factors, such as pigments derived from body wastes, arrangement of scales, and even light, must come into play. ■ Many butterflies give off the odor of flowers,

Detail of wing, greatly magnified, showing the overlapping scales. The shapes of scales vary even on the same wing. (A) Other types of scales are shown at right; (B) is scent-secreting scale with tuft at its tip.

spices, or musk. These ethereal fragrances are secreted from special wing scales called androconia. They are usually longer and narrower than the other wing scales. In certain species, the androconia are grouped in spots or bands; in others, they are scattered on the surface of the upper wing. ■ It is mainly the males who use these love essences to attract the females. But the females of some species also secrete scents. Although their fragrances cannot be detected by man, the males can sense them at great distances by means of the olfactory cavities located on the antennae. Most scent-giving males are butterflies while scent-giving females are nearly always various species of moths. ■

The male Agrias lugens *from Peru has scent tufts on his hind wings. The male* Papilio childrenae oedippus *of Colombia has white scent scales on the open marginal folds of his hind wing.*

Agrias lugens

Papilio childrenae oedippus

The male Glover's Silkworm (Samia gloveri, *western North America*) has olfactory sense organs on his antennae. He can find his newborn mate even as she emerges from her cocoon. She secretes a scent from a gland on her tail.

Female emerging from cocoon

■ The amorous play of Lepidoptera varies with the species. Only recently have scientists studied it in a few species, and there is still much to learn. ■ During the mating season Lepidoptera reach their peak of sensory reaction. Male and female nocturnal moths find each other by scent. In some species, the male can detect the scent of a female from more than half a mile away, if even a light wind is blowing in his direction. ■ The female of some species mates only once in her lifetime. After mating she no longer gives off a scent, and no male will approach her. ■ The diurnal butterflies find each other by sight, and experiments show that males can be lured by bits of colored paper. Not until the butterfly is close to the paper does his olfactory sense tell him that he is mistaken in his attentions. ■ Butterflies and moths are among the insects which undergo a complete metamorphosis of four stages. The female lays eggs from which the caterpillars, or larvae, hatch. The larvae change into pupae, or chrysalids, from which the adults emerge. ■ The female butterfly or moth lays her eggs on the plant which will later nourish the larvae —the swallowtail on carrot for instance, the tortoise-shell on nettle. Her botanical foresight of the larva's needs is an unsolved mystery of what scientists call innate behavior.

Eggs, greatly magnified. These vary in shape and color according to species and genus. LEFT TO RIGHT: Samia gloveri, Vanessa, Pieris, Limenitis.

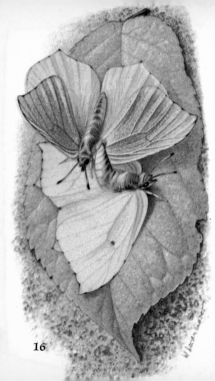

■ The female finds the right food plant by using the delicate sensory organs in her antennae and in her feet. ■ The eggs, varying in shape according to genus and species, are placed on the food plant either singly or in groups. Again, depending on the species, the caterpillars may hatch in a week, or, if the eggs overwinter, in months. ■ The main function of the caterpillar is to grow, and to this end it eats ravenously. When it gets too big for its skin, it molts. ■ The egg and larval stages are the most vulnerable times in the lives of Lepidoptera, for it is then that they are most subject to disease or to predatory attack by other insects or birds. ■ When the caterpillar has reached its full growth, it makes a chrysalis or spins a cocoon. There are three types of pupae: the free chrysalid in which the insect retains considerable freedom of movement of head parts, limbs, and abdominal segment; the incomplete type in which the insect is much less mobile;

During the courtship of the lemon butterfly (Gonepteryx cleopatra, southern Europe) the male runs over the outspread wings of the female. He is alternately caught and released between her suddenly uplifted wings.

16

and the mummy pupa in which the adult must develop while completely immobile, except for the abdominal segment, until the hour of emergence (see the front end sheets). ▪ The damp adult comes out of the pupa with limply hanging wings. It pumps air and green blood into its wings, forcing them open to their full spread. The wings dry and harden, and the blood is drawn back into the body. The whole process of drying and getting the wings ready for flight may take several hours. ▪ During the first moments of flight, the butterfly or moth releases a spurt of red or brown fluid from its posterior. This fluid contains the waste materials which accumulated in the intestinal tract while the insect was in the pupal case. ▪

Climate may influence the appearance of certain Lepidoptera. ABOVE: *The rainy season form of* Precis octavia *of Central Africa.* BELOW: *The dry season form of the same butterfly.*

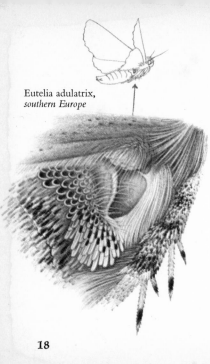

Eutelia adulatrix,
southern Europe

Now the final stage of its life has been reached, the time in which it must mate and lay eggs to perpetuate the species. ■ The adult, or imago, is now finished with growth. It is bound within its articulated chitinous covering—its exoskeleton—like a knight within his armor. ■ Inside its body the butterfly or moth has muscles, nerves, a vascular system with green blood, a digestive system, air tubes, sexual organs, and well-developed sensory organs. ■ The adult Lepidoptera have large compound eyes composed of from 4,000 to 30,000 faceted lenses. The olfactory cavities of the antennae may be equally numerous. Highly sensitive taste organs are located not only in the proboscis but also on the slender legs. ■ The six legs are attached to the thorax, one pair to each segment. The front pair of legs in many species of butterflies has been modified into "cleaning paws" with which they groom themselves. ■ The wings of butterflies and moths are also attached to the thorax and are moved by thoracic muscles. ■

Hearing organ, enlarged, of a night-flying moth, located on the thorax. The scales and hair surrounding the eardrum, or tympanum, form an ear.

18

The ability to hear high frequency sounds, such as those sent out by bats, helps moths escape from their hungry, night-flying predators. There is even speculation that sounds emitted by certain moths may jam the bats' "radar" system.

The front and back wings are arranged so that they brace each other in flight. Their position at rest—especially in moths—varies from family to family, and is characteristic. ■ When there are color differences between male and female Lepidoptera, the male is generally the more beautiful. The female's inconspicuous coloration, as with birds, seems to have a biological purpose, possibly to provide her, the mother of the race, with greater protection. Sexual dimorphism, or differences of form, structure, or color between males and females of the same species, has sometimes led scientists to believe they are of two different species. ■ Temperature and climate may also influence the actual physical appearance of certain species. ■

Catocala fraxini, *Europe*

The spring brood which emerges from over-wintering eggs, larvae, or pupae, may be different in color from the brood which hatches later in the summer. Another example of such seasonal dimorphism is the difference of appearance between the rainy season generation and the dry season generation of certain species. ■ To sustain life, it seems to be necessary for living things to kill. Plants depend on inorganic substances, animals eat plants, predators eat herbivorous animals and each other. All living things prey upon other living things and, in turn, are preyed upon. ■ Whoever is best armed for this struggle for existence has the best chance to survive—but in nature there are kinds of arms. The weapons of the weak are not those of the strong. Butterflies and moths cannot attack; they can only defend themselves. If danger threatens, they take hurried flight, feign death, or creep under leaves. Many of them have marvelous ways of camouflaging themselves. Others try to scare off the enemy with simulated danger signals, or try to impress him with brave gestures. ■ The Greek word for actor is *mimos*, from which comes the word "mimicry." In zoology, mimicry refers to the resemblance of an animal to the shapes and colors of its surroundings or to other animals. Many moths at rest look like the pieces of wood, bark, or lichen on which they have

For some yet unknown reason, certain nocturnal moths are compulsively attracted to light. The females of many species are not so attracted until after they have laid their eggs. Butterflies may also be attracted to light in the daytime and may dash themselves into mountain snow fields or onto the shining surface of a body of water.

ABOVE: Porthesia similis, *Europe, North America,* Tussock Moth
CENTER: Philosamea cynthis, *Eurasia, North America*
Ailanthus Silkworm BELOW: Geometra papilionaria, *Europe*

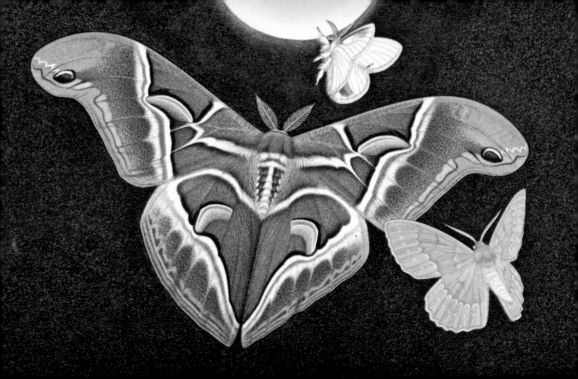

alighted. Sometimes they resemble spots on fungi, dangerous mouth openings, or even dew-drops. ■ Certain nocturnal species remain so well hidden during the day that they would still be unknown to scientists if they had not been caught at night with a decoy light. ■ Some species of butterflies and moths have wings that not only look like leaves but even bear the venation of those leaves, though it may not correspond to their own. ■ Other Lepidoptera make use of flash or "scare" colors. At rest they are inconspicuous, but when they are disturbed they suddenly spread out their hind wings on which there are glaring colors or eye-shaped spots. In this way they startle their enemies and get time to escape. ■ Some species have tail-parts that look like heads; their enemies will sometimes be fooled into making their first attack on the less vulnerable regions of the butterfly's or moth's body and spare the real head with its sensory organs. ■

Protective coloration in moths. Their color patterns are so broken up that, at rest, it is almost impossible to see the shape of their bodies. The moth at the left is Duomitius leuconotus *which is found in India and Indonesia.*

Thysania zenobia,
Central and South America

Anophylla includaria,
Brazil

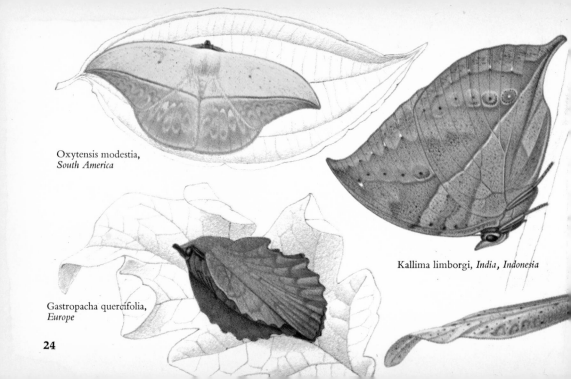

Oxytensis modestia,
South America

Kallima limborgi, *India, Indonesia*

Gastropacha quercifolia,
Europe

Certain species of butterflies and moths not only simulate the colors and forms of leaves but sometimes carry the deception to the point of copying the venation of leaves, even though it may differ from their own venation.

Copiopteryx derceto, *Brazil*

Some Lepidoptera chirp or make rattling sounds when they are threatened, but scientists have not yet determined the value of such sounds in defense. ■ Protective coloration, which permits the butterfly or moth to merge into its surroundings, is effected by the breaking up, and thus making unrecognizable, the otherwise telltale characteristics of the insect's shape. It is called somatolysis. ■ This type of camouflage has evoked much discussion among scientists. If, in nature, creatures of thousands of different forms and color patterns are generated, will those species protected by camouflage or mimicry be best able to survive, whereas others not thus protected will be gradually culled out by ever-present, hungry predators? ■

Members of the family Arctiidae are protected by the disagreeable taste of their body secretions. This particular moth, Amastus episcotosia *of Central America, has a warning pattern which resembles a head on its abdomen.*

Automeris nyctimene,
Colombia, Brazil

Automeris pyrrhomelas,
Colombia

When disturbed while at rest, some species of normally inconspicuous appearance suddenly flash their hindwings, revealing eye spots. This may startle the enemy and give the moth time to escape.

DEFENSE MECHANISMS OF LEPIDOPTERA

adult mimicry

Dicranura vinula, *Europe*

Delias ligata, *New Guinea*

Heliconius cydno hermogenes, *Colombia*

Conspicuous warning colors indicating they are poisonous or bad-tasting.

Saddleback caterpillar Sibine stimulea, *United States poisonous spines*

28

Panaxia quadripunctaria, *Europe*

Psaphis euschemoides, *India*

There are still other protective devices found among Lepidoptera. The caterpillars of some species have conspicuous warning colors. If, in spite of these colors, they are gobbled up by a reptile or bird, they are immediately spit out. The predator cannot stand their taste and soon learns to avoid them. ■ One of the tussock moth caterpillars has a thick covering of hair; when danger threatens it rolls itself up like a porcupine. ■ Many hawk moth caterpillars are able to draw in their heads and to inflate the front of their bodies, thus showing the enemy the striking eyespots on the side of their bodies. ■ The multiplicity of protective devices is well illustrated in the Puss Moth. The caterpillar defends itself by biting and by spraying acid from openings in the neck. It has a motley scare-color pattern. It can also extend bizarre spiral threads from its tail. The adult moth, on the other hand, is nondescript and is protected only by mimicry of its surroundings. ■

ABOVE LEFT: *The Puss Moth caterpillar,* Dicranura vinula, *Europe, defends itself by biting, and spraying acid. It also has a scare-color pattern, and can extend spiral threads from its tail.* BELOW: *The caterpillar of* Dasychira pudibunda, *Europe, has no weapons and can only bluff.*

The curious phenomenon of mimicry reaches its height when one species imitates another "protected" species. In such a case, a defenseless animal takes on the guise of an aggressive or protected animal, sometimes joining the company of its model and even acting like it. ■ Harmless butterflies and moths fly with poisonous or bad-tasting ones. One moth mimics a wasp; another is patterned after a hornet. A well-known example of mimicry is found in two butterflies of North America, the Monarch and the Viceroy. The Monarch is shunned by birds, presumably because of its bad taste. The Viceroy, which looks like the Monarch and associates with it, is thus protected by its appearance. ■ The Viceroy does not look at all

The Brazilian Owlet Moth not only imitates the appearance of the dangerous and furry silkworm but also mimics its jerky movements.

Pseudosphex ichneumoneus, *Bolivia*
*This harmless moth resembles
an aggressive wasp.*

like any other member of its family, the Admirals, but it still does fly like them. When it glides, its wings are held out straight; on the other hand the Monarch glides with its wings held in a slightly upward-angled position. Apparently, however, predators are not able to see this distinction between the Viceroy and the milkweed butterfly, the protected Monarch. ■ Since the initial investigations of Charles Darwin, attempts by man to explain mimicry have not led to universally accepted conclusions. Imitation may well be only a form that originated by accident, a random hereditary change that made an individual somewhat resemble a species that has protective coloration. This advantage would help it survive and would also aid in the survival of its descendants which looked most like the imitated species. ■

Melittia bombyliformis, *Asia, a clearwing moth, looks like a dangerous hornet.*

Morpho papirius, *Peru*

Morpho cypris, *Colombia*

Wing movements of a butterfly in flight

■ Flying insects have evolved from wingless creatures. ■ The wings of butterflies and moths, unlike those of bats and birds, are not modified limbs. They develop from protuberances on the wall of the back and are flat chitinous structures containing veins or ribs, blood vessels, spiracles and nerves. ■ In flight, most butterflies use a flutter and glide pattern with a wingbeat of from five to twelve strokes per second. Most moths, especially the hawk moths, have a continuously rapid flight with a wingbeat of from 40 to 85 strokes per second. ■

Morpho anaxibia, *Brazil*

The Morpho butterflies of tropical South America are particularly lovely in flight, flashing brilliant iridescent colors produced by refraction of light on their wings.

33

Protoparce pellenia, *Colombia*

■ Butterflies, with their erratic flight, can cover six to nine miles in an hour, but moths can reach distances of 34 miles in an hour, and, when helped by a tailwind, can catch up with ships and trains. ■ During courtship play and when sucking nectar from flowers, butterflies and moths can hover in flight, seemingly suspended in air. ■ Certain moths, such as those of the Sphingidae, which come out at dusk to feed, have only a very brief time in which to eat before darkness falls. They must rush from flower to flower getting enough nectar for their needs. ■

The Sphingidae generally have such a rapid wingbeat that, in flight, their wings can be perceived only as shadowy shapes.

The Micropteryx ammanella of Europe is a primitive moth which has chewing jaws and eats pollen. It is one of the very few Lepidoptera that eats rather than sucks in its food.

Traditionally, we think of Lepidoptera as feeders on the nectar of flowers. Actually, many kinds of butterflies and moths visit no flowers whatsoever but live on the sap of trees and plants, on the juice of fermenting fruits, or even on dung. ■ The Death's Head Moth invades beehives and robs them of honey. ■ There are a few species of noctuids found in Asia and Africa which live on the tears of antelope and cattle. At night they hang in clusters around the animals' eyes and thrust their proboscises under the animals' eyelids. It is thought that diseases of cattle may be transmitted by these moths because of their peculiar drinking habits.

Cocytinus lucifer, *Brazil, one of the Sphingidae, has a proboscis ten inches long, three times its body length.*

35

Many butterflies of the tropical forests spend most of their lives flying just above the treetops. They come to ground level only to get food and water and to lay their eggs.

Papilio brookiana of Indonesia in flight and (right) sucking nectar from a flower.

Lepidoptera seem to require large amounts of water. Some night-flying species drink from dewdrops; the day-flying butterflies drink from moist earth, puddles, or river banks. Some species, such as the swallowtails and blues, assemble in dense masses to drink. As many as 100 to 200 butterflies gather in these swarms. ■ Many Lepidoptera are most often seen among the beautiful but immobile flowers. Certain species of both butterflies and moths use flower nectar for food. In getting the nectar, they incidentally assist in the pollination of the flowers, but not, however, to the same extent as bees. ■ For some still unknown reason, butterflies are able to identify flowers by color, and seem to have a preference for red ones. When they draw near to the flowers, they are also attracted by scent. ■ Nocturnal moths find their food supply mainly by smell, using the olfactory cells on their antennae. ■ Individuals of some species establish definite "feeding territories" in particularly desirable areas and will try to chase away any Lepidoptera that invade them. ■ Many butterflies perch to feed; many moths hover. ■ Certain of the primitive species of moths have functional jaws instead of a proboscis. They do not suck in liquid food, but eat pollen. ■ There are also some butterflies and moths that never eat during their entire adult life; their sucking organs are either rudimentary or absent. The giant silkworms, such as the Cecropia and Promethea moths, are perhaps the best known examples. They do not live long; during their brief lifespan they are nourished only by the fat retained in their bodies from the larval through the pupal stages. A brief mating season (which may in part explain to us their urgency in finding a mate), a quick deposition of eggs, and they have vanished from the dance of life. ■

MIGRATORY RANGE OF THE MONARCH

Seattle

Los Angeles

New York

Miami

breeding ground   winter distribution

summer distribution

winter resting places on "butterfly trees"

Being winged creatures, butterflies and moths have the ability to travel wherever they wish, but most of them spend their whole lives in the area where they were born. A few species, however, are migratory and undertake tremendous journeys. ■ Among those North American butterflies which make long migratory flights, some up to 2,000 miles, are the Monarch and the Painted Lady ■ The Monarchs take fairly definite routes on their annual migrations. These routes are now being studied by scientists, who are banding the wings of Monarchs at their breeding grounds in Canada. In September, large flocks of Monarchs gather in New England. Then they travel south, usually in small groups, along the coast to Florida. There they winter, most often in pine trees.

Scientists are banding Monarchs on their wings in order to study their migrations. These butterflies, like most migratory birds, travel south in the fall, north in the spring.

They seem to winter in the same trees each season. ■ On the West Coast, Monarchs fly south to rest in their "butterfly trees" in California. On cool or cloudy days they remain on the tree; on sunny warm days they fly about looking for food. ■ With the advent of spring they fly north, laying eggs on milkweed plants along the way. It is thought that many adults never reach the northern breeding grounds; their children, hatched from the eggs laid en route, complete the journey, and possibly it is their children's children which again travel south in the fall. ■ Monarchs are found in many parts of the world, even in the Far East. ■

The Monarch Danaus plexippus *is a species which makes long migrations. Shunned by birds, it is one of the few so-called protected species. The harmless Viceroy,* Limenitis archippus, *looks like and associates with the Monarch. The White Admiral,* Limentis arthemis, *is closely related to the Viceroy but does not look at all like it.*

Danaus plexippus

Limenitis archippus

Limenitis arthemis

■ Unlike the Monarch and some other migratory species, the Painted Lady does not migrate seasonally. It apparently moves at irregular intervals, either because of overcrowding or because of a lack of food. When it does migrate, it may journey as far as 1,400 miles. Great masses of Painted Ladies have been seen moving at about eight miles an hour. ■ The Painted Lady is one of the few butterflies which is found in almost every country in the world, but its migrations have thus far been charted only in Europe and North America. ■ Migrating butterflies are sometimes seen hitching rides on boats and planes. They have also been sighted flying over oceans. ■ Some of the European Lepidoptera which migrate are the Death's Head Moth, *Acherontia atropos*, the Red Admiral Butterfly, *Vanessa atalanta*, and the charming little Dovetail, *Macroglossum stellaratum*, which looks so much like the hummingbirds of the Americas as it whirs among the summer flowers. ■ The reasons for such migrations by Lepidoptera are apparently similar to the reasons for bird migrations; probably to secure an adequate food supply. But, as yet, they are far from being understood by scientists. ■ Many Lepidoptera fly from North Africa and southern Europe to northern Europe in the spring, even crossing the seemingly impenetrable barrier of the Alps. They, or possibly their children, somehow manage to make a return trip in the fall to avoid the cold of winter. ■ On the other hand, certain species of both moths and butterflies are able to survive the winter. Some overwinter as eggs, others spend the winter as larvae, pupae, or even as adults. ■

The Painted Lady, Vanessa cardui, *also a famous migratory butterfly, is found in so many parts of the world that it is known as a cosmopolite.*

Vanessa cardui
Vanessa cardui japonica
Vanessa cardui kershawi
→ *spring or summer migration*
→ *fall migration*
● *Painted Ladies seen in flight over open oceans*

Because of the extensive migrations of the Painted Lady only two geographical races have developed: cardui japonica of Japan and East China (a similar form is found on West Java); and cardui kershawi of Australia and New Zealand.

Frost Moth, Erannis defolaria, *Europe*

female

male

The Giant Frost Moth appears in November when most insects are dead or dormant.

Only the male Bagworm has wings; the wingless female remains in the cocoon, even laying her eggs in it.

caterpillars in "bag"

female

male

Bagworm,
Pachythelia unicolor,
Europe

■ When most insects have died, migrated, or hibernated because of the cold, the Giant Frost Moth of Europe appears in the November twilight, searching for the stubwinged female of its species. The larvae, which emerge in the spring, damage fruit trees. They pupate in the ground, letting themselves down to the earth by silken threads. ■ In the spring, the larvae of bagworms build a bag of leaves in which they live and eventually pupate. Only the males, short-lived and wild in flight, come out of these bags; the females are flightless. Mating takes place within the bag, and in the bag, too, the eggs are laid. ■ Parthenogenesis, the development of a new generation of females from unfertilized eggs, is not uncommon in this family. ■ One of the most unusual moths is the European *Hydrocampa nymphaeata* which lives under water. The caterpillar spins itself a quiver-like case which it fastens to the stem of an underwater plant. It then lives in this case, reaching out to gnaw on water plants. ■ When it is ready to pupate, it builds a similar silken case, also under water, with small openings at the place where the case is fastened to the plant stem. Through these holes the pupa is able to get enough air to supply its needs while it is in its little diving bell. ■ When the adult is ready to emerge, it gathers under its still unfolded wings all of the air available in the pupal case, and, buoyed up by this air, shoots up to the surface of the water. During the ascent, a fine white covering of wax, which keeps the wings from getting wet, is stripped off. This wax rises to the surface and momentarily stands upright in the water. Males above the surface are alerted by this little white wax column, and rush to see if a female has emerged. ■

A rarity in the world of butterflies and moths is this European moth which spends much of its life cycle under water.

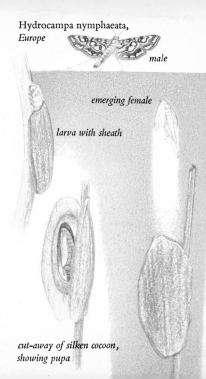

Hydrocampa nymphaeata,
Europe

male

emerging female

larva with sheath

*cut-away of silken cocoon,
showing pupa*

Each butterfly and moth, no matter how unpretentious, is an incomprehensible miracle—a challenge to the ever inquiring mind of man. Still one of life's greatest wonders is metamorphosis—the transformation of the often ugly caterpillar into dormant pupa from which at last emerges the beautiful imago. A similar metamorphosis, man likes to think, lies in store for him when death comes at last and he takes leave of the chrysalis of life. ■ In his last sermon before his death, Buddha spoke thus to the butterflies: "I thank you, you are my masters. From you I have learned more than from all the writings of the Brahmans." ■

Parnassius charltonius, an Apollo butterfly, is found only in the Himalayas from seventeen to twenty thousand feet above sea level. The female comes down to lower regions, where the larval food plants grow, only to lay her eggs.

INDEX

Arctiidae

Lymantriidae

Nymphalidae

Sphingidae

Noctuidae

Lasiocampidae

Butterflies usually rest with their wings over their back as shown above. Moths rest with their wings outspread or folded tent-like over their back. Shown here are characteristic resting positions for some of the families.